Bang Out of Order!

Johnny Carrington and Danny Sturrock

Bang Out of Order!

By Johnny Carrington and Danny Sturrock.

Authors' acknowledgements:

We would like to thank:
Mandy and Sophie for all their support and our families for their encouragement and patience.
The original cast: Gemma Aked-Priestley, Charlotte Bath, Bethan Frecknall, Shaun Gradidge, Leon Humphreys and Michael Mears. You are all stars!
Mark Wheeller for his enthusiasm and faith in our project.
Jackie Compton and all at Southampton City Council.
Tim Ford for showing us that less is in fact more!
Paul Mills, Head of Drama, Westgate School Winchester.
Mrs. Sarah Howells, Head Teacher, Oaklands Community School.
Roger Burlinson, Maximus Productions.
April Newton for always being there to help.
Our Techie's - Amy Barnett, Matt Griffiths and, in particular, Aaron Dadd, who, in all fairness, did manage to stay awake for 'most' of our performances.
The parents of the cast and crew who have been so supportive and tolerant of rehearsals etc right from the start.
Evie and all at dbda for all your hard work.
Sophie Gorrell-Barnes and all at MBA.

Enquiries regarding all rights associated with this play, including performing rights, should be addressed to:
Sophie Gorell Barnes, MBA Literary Agents Limited, 62 Grafton Way, London. W1P 5LD. Tel: 020 7387 2076. Email Sophie@mbalit.co.uk

First edition published by dbda in 2007

ISBN 978 1 902843 21 6

BRITISH LIBRARY CATALOGUING IN PUBLICATION DATA
A catalogue record for this book is available from the British Library.

© Johnny Carrington & Danny Sturrock - 2007
The moral right of the authors has been asserted.

No part of this publication may be transmitted, stored in a retrieval system or reproduced in any form or by means electronic, mechanical, photocopying, typescript, recording or otherwise, without prior permission of the copyright owners.

Photocopying of scripts is illegal! Even if you hold a licence from the Copyright Licensing Agency you are only allowed to photocopy up to a total of 5% of the whole script. Please remember the writers who depend upon their share of your purchases... without them the plays which you perform could not have been written or published.

Further copies of this publication can be purchased from:
dbda ltd, Pin Point, Rosslyn Crescent, Harrow HA1 2SU.
Tel: 0870 333 7771   Fax: 0870 333 7772   E-mail: info@dbda.co.uk

I was approached by Johnny Carrington and Danny Sturrock from Oaklands Community School in Lordshill, Southampton in 2005 regarding a play that they had written called 'Bang Out of Order'. The play sought to address the issues of anti-social behaviour (ASB) involving both young and older generations. As the investigator of anti-social behaviour for the West of the city of Southampton, where the school is based, I felt that the play was the missing link in getting the message across to all age groups. All too often young people are seen as the problem, not the solution, and to involve them could only help deal with the issues. I also felt that with the wider audience it would make the older generation understand that not all young people are the same, moreover, that it is sometimes the attitude of these older people that causes the problems.

Myself and a colleague from the Police read the play and apart from a few minor amendments regarding legislation we felt it was very well written and would get across the impacts of ASB in the community. On reading it I found it quite strange that I could actually put names of real people to the characters! I nominated the play for a Home Office 'Taking a stand award' and, due to its no holds barred tackling of ASB issues, it won!

People of all ages who have seen the play find it very thought provoking, and some even found it quite emotional. I am very proud to have been part of this process and would encourage others to look at how, without lecturing and leaflets, messages can be spread across communities.

Jackie Compton
Senior Investigator, Community Safety Team
Southampton City Council

Introduction

On a school trip, walking back to our apartment following a performance at the National Student Drama Festival (NSDF) in Scarborough, we began talking about writing something of our own. Having both performed at various improvisation evenings together, we both decided that we shared a common appreciation of theatre and, although at times a bit twisted, a sense of humour! Two years later, that process started and 'Bang Out of Order' began to take shape.

Working in education, we both wanted to tackle an issue that was relevant to the youth that we worked with on a daily basis. We decided we would try and write a play about something that confronted so many people; both young and old. For a long time, anti-social behaviour has been a problem in many places; no less so than in the area of our school. However, in tackling the issue we wanted to be sure that we weren't 'taking sides'. All too often this problem is one of perception; a struggle between different ages. Confrontation can often occur because of a lack of communication. Paramount in our work from the very early stages was the need to make this play 'accessible' to all ages and in a way that did not 'lecture' or make swinging moral judgements. This we felt would have been a sure fire way of switching off our intended audience. To help facilitate this we felt that humour, multi-media, dance and music were all going to play an important part in the performance.

Right from the beginning we decided to work with a small number of pupils from the Oaklands Able Pupil Project (APP). We felt it would stretch the students artistically if they were asked to multi-role. A simple on-stage costume change, symbolising their new character was all that was needed. Moreover, these quick changes were consistently commented on in adjudications, and noted for their effectiveness and simplicity. Each week the students were presented with a new section of script, and it is to their credit that they took the various changes and re-writes without complaint (well not too much). Three months after we started there was the first of many final drafts. Trying to make an impact, we managed to get a real car into our theatre for part of the set. This was, as you can imagine, a great source of interest and helped promote the show. We opened to good houses and some excellent reviews.

Powerful Youth Production with Plenty to Say

Bang Out of Order, a powerful original play exploring the issues surrounding antisocial behaviour, has won local drama festival awards. And it is easy to see why. It is a complex and well crafted piece of alternative community theatre, combining comedy as a perfect counterfoil to its tragic elements. The cast of six youngsters were committed, disciplined and passionate in their performances, creating an ensemble of confrontation yet vulnerable characters with which the audience could identify and empathise.

Atmospheric lighting on an austere metal set created intriguing shadows, enhancing the dramatic nature of the play. Film projections and appropriate soundtracks provided an outlet for slapstick, action or tension. Moments of frivolity added poignancy to the heartbreak that followed. This impressive production both entertained and challenged, and deserves to do well at the Edinburgh (Fringe) Festival later in the summer.

Anne Waggott, Southern Daily Echo

Following this success it was decided to compete in local festivals where we were fortunate to pick up various awards. It also gave us the confidence to take our show to, perhaps the toughest festival in the world, the Edinburgh Fringe Festival. We secured an excellent venue and 'all' that held us back was money. Here, Southampton City Council proved invaluable. We had initially approached the Southampton City Council Community Safety Team for help and legal advice. Now we approached them hat in hand, and they came up trumps!

Finance was now secure, but now we had to make our show 'transferable'. To this end, a debt of gratitude must go to Tim Ford from the Birmingham Rep. A friend of many years and who had been with us on our NSDF excursions, he radically suggested transferring all the action from a large expansive set to one scaled down scaffolding tower. Suddenly all our actors were crawling, jumping and sliding around the tower that became our composite set.

Introduction

Whilst this helped in many ways, it left us with a dilemma that had to be solved. How was AD (the character now known as Steph) going to fall? In previous productions the character had fallen from a tower on stage to a large high jump mat off stage. Now, space restrictions, and the need to build and strike a set in five minutes necessitated something much quicker. After much deliberation and experimentation a combination of projected images, smoke, slow motion and a good sense of balance from the actor who played AD, gave us a 'fall' that has been commented on as a really powerful theatrical 'moment'. We would advise any future directors to try for themselves different solutions. Be bold, be adventurous, but be safe.

As a festival play, we have found Bang Out of Order to be very successful. We picked up awards at every festival we entered including the Youth Challenge Cup for the Southern Division of the British One Act Play Festival. We would really advise groups to take the opportunities on offer for multi-media, as we would for the dance/choreographed routines. These sections bring such life and energy to the performance and offer the chance for some cross-curricular activities.

Several of our GCSE students saw a number of the performances and wanted to do a shortened version for the Edexcel Paper II exam. As a result, we have included the cuts that would suit a performance of approximately 20 minutes for four candidates. Although very suitable for GCSE, Bang Out of Order has also been used on the B-Tech National Diploma.

This has been a very busy last year for both of us. At the time of writing this, it was almost a year ago when the cast received their first 'final' draft of the script. The difference from that draft to the published version is huge. The play, originally written for six actors (3m and 3f), has now been reduced to work with four actors (2m and 2f). Some characters have changed and scenes have been added and lost which we feel makes the play even stronger now. The emotional journey of performing at so many different venues culminating in the fringe has been fraught, but immensely satisfying.

We would like to thank everyone who has been instrumental in the success of Bang Out of Order so far (you know who you are!), particularly the original cast and crew who worked tirelessly and with a never-ending enthusiasm.

We hope that anyone who chooses to use Bang Out of Order in the future will have as much fun working on this piece as we did and that it will make the actors and audience alike think about the issue's that the piece explores.

Johnny Carrington and Danny Sturrock
January 2007

Photographs from the original production

Above: (From L-R) Gemma Aked-Priestley (Stacey), Bethan Frecknall (Steph) and Shaun Gradidge (Mouse).

Left: (From L-R) Michael Mears (Ollie), Leon Humphreys (AD), Shaun Gradidge (Mouse).

Above: (From L-R) Drinking Scene, Shaun Gradidge (Mouse) and Michael Mears (Ollie).

Above: (Clockwise from Top Left) Intimidation - Bethan Frecknall (Steph), Shaun Gradidge (Mouse), Gemma Aked-Priestley (Mrs Harris) and Michael Mears (Ollie).

Left: (From L-R) Charlotte Bath (Keeley) and Michael Mears (Ollie).

Bang Out of Order!

Original Cast List

Bang Out of Order was premiered by Oaklands Community School's - Able Pupil Project on Wednesday 8th March 2006 with the following cast:

Ollie	Michael Mears
Mouse/Mr Harris/Teacher	Shaun Gradidge
AD/Ollie's Dad	Leon Humphreys
Keeley	Charlotte Bath
Stacey/Mrs Harris	Gemma Aked-Priestley
Steph/Ollie's Mum	Bethan Frecknall

Director(s)	Johnny Carrington & Danny Sturrock
Lighting	Aaron Dadd
Sound	Amy Barnett
Multimedia	Danny Sturrock

Productions of Bang Out of Order should use minimal props and setting so that the pace of the play is not interrupted by lengthy scene changes. These changes should be incorporated into the scenes using choreographed sequences and/or underscored pre-recorded music.

Cast list for the 4 player version: 2m/2f

Actor 1: (Male)	Ollie
Actor 2: (Male)	Mouse/ Mr Harris/ Phillip (Ollie's dad)
Actor 3: (Female)	Keeley; Mrs Harris
Actor 4: (Female)	Steph; Sue (Ollie's step-mum)

The play starts with a darkened stage. There is a raised scaffold construction centre stage with four scaffolding legs extended at each corner. At the foot of each leg, there should be a single floor light facing diagonally in towards the centre of the scaffolding. These lights can be used to create interesting shadows, but also angled to light the faces of the actors that are standing on top of the scaffolding platform.

CCTV style video images are projected onto a screen, at the rear of the stage, showing groups of youths hanging around shops and on the streets dressed in hoodies and caps, etc. Appropriately menacing music plays over to top of this (a mix of *The Prodigy's – Their Law* was used in the original production). As the beat begins, a group of youths suddenly dart on stage and create a menacing tableau on the scaffold. They exit just as quickly before re-entering to make another, but equally intimidating, tableau. This process can be repeated.

The beat of the music changes again and the group split up and race around the stage spraying graffiti on walls, drinking and damaging property. One of the group picks up a bottle and throws it and smashes an imaginary window at the rear of the theatre. Computer graphics of a bottle smashing through glass were created for this moment and projected onto the rear of the stage wall. At this point they all freeze momentarily, then slowly and sinisterly turn to face the audience, as if an audience member had shouted at them. They all slowly start to walk towards the audience, each repeating a short threatening line to a member of the audience with increasing hostility. These lines should be repeated at least 6 times, the last being filled with anger. Once this has happened, the group quickly disperse as if the police have arrived, perhaps with a chorally spoken "Shit! Old bill".

Subtle lights fade up on the raised scaffold. Mouse and Keeley become Michael and Sharon Harris, a couple in their late 50s who also live on the estate. The change of character is signified by Mouse removing his hoody and putting on some glasses and Stacey replacing her hoody with a cardigan. Sharon is sitting reading a book and Michael is flicking through a newspaper.

Mr Harris:	Here Sharon, listen to this.
Mrs Harris:	What's that?
Mr Harris:	*(Reading an article from his newspaper)* "A council defended its decision today to evict a family from their privately rented home in Oxford. Phillip Hammond and Sue Warner were originally served with a warning following the antisocial conduct of Mr Hammond's 16 year old son, Oliver. Oliver Hammond was the subject of an Anti-Social Behaviour Order last December for spitting and swearing at neighbours, causing damage to property, theft and consistently causing alarm and distress to local residents. Oxford County Council initially refused to re-house the family, saying Mr Hammond had made them 'intentionally homeless' by failing to control his son." Now you tell me this, why aren't they doing that round here? I can think of plenty of yobs that need evicting.
Mrs Harris:	What good does it really do though?
Mr Harris:	A lot, if it means they are off our doorstep.
Mrs Harris:	Yes, but that just means that some other poor sods are going to end up with them. It doesn't solve the problem, Michael.
Mr Harris:	Well, maybe not, but it's a bloody good start I say. *(He gets up to go to the window.)* I mean, just look at them.
Mrs Harris:	Will you come away from that window!

Mr Harris:	Who do they think they are, eh? Shouting, screaming and drinking in the streets till all hours.
Mrs Harris:	Times have changed.
Mr Harris:	Too bloody right they have! Well, it's about time someone went and said something. *(He throws down his newspaper and goes to leave.)*
Mrs Harris:	Don't you dare!
Mr Harris:	Why not! I'm not being a prisoner in my own home just because of that lot.
Mrs Harris:	If you go out there and start stirring things up, then that makes us a target. I don't want a brick through my window!
Mr Harris:	That's exactly why they think they can run riot 24 hours a day, because no one says anything.
Mrs Harris:	Please, don't go out there! I'm serious!
Mr Harris:	Fine. Let them destroy everything. (He raises his voice and shouts out the window) Bloody yobs!

As Mr Harris turns and walks away from the window to sit down, the sound of smashing glass can be heard as a bottle smashes through the window. He ducks down covering his head, then looks up to face his wife.

Mr Harris:	Right, that's it! *(He exits.)*

The lights fade to black and Mrs Harris also exits.

The lights fade up and we see Ollie in his bedroom getting ready for school. His stepmother can be heard off stage shouting up the stairs to him.

Sue:	*(Offstage)* Ollie are you up… Ollie?!
Ollie:	*(Slightly abrupt)* I'm getting ready.
Sue:	You better be. The bus goes in ten minutes.
Ollie:	*(Very abrupt)* Get off my case will ya, Sue.

Sue enters.

Sue:	No I won't. This is important Ollie. It's our last chance to make a fresh start. *(Pause)* Are you listening to me? There are no more second chances. If you slip up now…
Ollie:	*(Interrupting Sue and pushing past her.)* I've got to go, I don't want to miss my bus now, do I?
Sue:	(Shouting after him) Ollie… Ollie!

This scene suddenly changes as loud urban music plays. (A Mix of **Dizzee Rascal's – Fix Up Look Sharp** *was used in the original production.) The actor playing Sue now throws on a Hoody and Baseball Cap to become Steph. She is joined by Ollie, Mouse and Keeley. A stylised choreographed movement sequence follows illustrating a group of young people waking up, getting dressed, having breakfast, etc. Ordinary mimes such as the brushing of teeth can be accented by quickly switching the mime into sticking their middle finger up at the audience, or using a can of deodorant to spray graffiti on walls, etc. There should be an element of menace in all that they do. Once they are all ready, they begin to make their way round to call for each other, except for Ollie who makes his own way to school. As they get to each house in turn, the following dialogue is spoken.*

Keeley:	Steph… We're going to be late!
Steph:	So what if we are?
Keeley:	We've got a test this morning dickhead… remember?
Steph:	So?

Keeley:	Oh I'm going without you then. *(They both join up with Mouse.)*
Mouse:	*(Calling off stage.)* Mum, have you made my sandwiches?... Thanks Mum *(He realises that Steph and Keeley are watching so shouts out to his Mum)* Oh you're so unfair!
	(They all begin to walk off to school when Mouse begins feeling guilty about being rude and runs back to his front door and whispers through the letter box) Sorry Mum. Won't be late... Love you!

Mouse, Keeley and Steph begin to make their way to school in the same stylised way. When they arrive, they sit outside of the school just before classes begin. They are all grouped together on the scaffolding. Steph sits playing with a lighter and her mobile phone. Mouse and Keeley start scribbling graffiti on one of the blocks with a marker.

Keeley:	Great, another shitty day at school.
Steph:	Bunk off then.
Keeley:	*(Getting a packet of cigarettes out of her pocket)* What, and get grounded again? No thanks. *(Going to light up a cigarette.)*
Mouse:	Give us a fag Keeley!
Keeley:	I've only got a couple left.
Steph:	Crap! You only bought them last night.
Keeley:	So? I've smoked 'em all?
Mouse:	Let's have a look then.
Keeley:	Why?

As Keeley finishes her line, Steph and Mouse grab the cigarettes off her and a game of piggy in the middle ensues as they count how many she really does have and take one each for themselves.

Mouse:	She's got loads in there!
Steph:	Told ya!

Keeley:	Steph give 'em back, don't be out of order... I'll tell Dad! *(Looks embarrassed.)*
Steph & Mouse:	Oh no! Not... Dad! *(Laughing)*
Steph:	Dad doesn't know you smoke!
Keeley:	*(Admitting defeat)* I wish you weren't my sister sometimes, you know that!

The bell goes and they start to make their way to lessons.

Mouse:	Have you heard about the new boy?
Keeley:	No.
Mouse:	Yeah, there's a new boy starting in our class, today!
Keeley:	Is he fit?
Mouse:	How do I know?
Keeley:	Well, knowing my luck, he'll be a right minger.

*At this point an excerpt from the **Romeo and Juliet Fantasy Overture** by Tchaikovsky gradually fades up as Ollie enters in a melodramatic manner. Some short stylised movement between Ollie and Keeley follows including mimed kisses being caught, Cupid's bow being fired etc to indicate that Keeley does in fact fancy him! The music scratches off and Ollie continues to walk across the stage, over to the group.*

| Keeley: | Coor, sex on legs or what! |
| Mouse: | Keeley, he's coming over! |

Ollie approaches the group. He's not sure where he needs to go.

Ollie:	Excuse me... I'm looking for the school office but I'm not quite sure where...
Mouse:	Are you the new boy?!
Ollie:	Well, yeah I guess.
Mouse:	Are you fit?!
Ollie:	What?

Keeley:	Mouse?!
Mouse:	Well, you wanted to know!
Steph:	What's your name then?
Ollie:	I'm Ollie, Ollie Hammond.
Mouse:	Why are you coming here now?
Ollie:	Well… um… I've just moved down from Oxford with my parents… My dad's got a new job… that's about it really.
Steph:	Oxford? It's a bit posh, isn't it?
Ollie:	What?
Keeley:	You're looking for the school office, yeah?
Ollie:	Yeah.
Keeley:	If you go through those doors, it's just on your left.
Ollie:	Nice one, cheers.

Ollie makes his way over to the office.

Mouse:	Are you going to say something to him then?
Keeley:	As if!
Mouse:	Go on!
Keeley:	I can't.
Mouse:	Yeah you can, come on, he's leaving.
Keeley:	You can't make me Mouse.
Mouse:	Yeah, you're right… Oi Ollie! Come here.
Keeley:	Mouse!
Mouse:	*(Ollie has now come over.)* Keeley wants to say something to you. *(Mouse just stands there giggling.)*

Steph walks off, clearly not impressed with Keeley's interest in Ollie. Not understanding what is going on, Mouse just stands there, between Ollie and Keeley. The other two are looking a bit sheepish but Mouse is just looking at them grinning.

Ollie:	Alright?
Keeley:	Alright?
Mouse:	Alright?

Awkward silence.

Keeley:	*(Kicking him in the shins.)* Mouse!!
Mouse:	What?!

It suddenly dawns on him that he should probably leave them to it and he runs off laughing.

Keeley:	Um… I was just going to say that… um… I can take you to the office if ya like?
Ollie:	It's OK, I'll find it, cheers anyway. *(Another awkward silence.)* I better be off. Better not be late.
Keeley:	Course. See ya.
Ollie:	See ya.

Keeley desperately wants to say something and just before Ollie exits she shouts across to him.

Keeley:	Wait a minute… do you want to come out with us tonight… *(Slight pause and then she starts to ramble.)* We normally meet up near the park.
	I mean if you don't want to, that's fine. After all, you've only just turned up at a new school and probably don't want to go out with us. But if you did want to go that would be gr… *(Ollie jumps in.)*
Ollie:	Yeah, OK. What do you normally do?
Keeley:	Well, not a lot really. Steph sometimes brings a few beers along… Mouse got a joint off his dad

	last week and we shared that… But normally we just chill and have a bit of a laugh.
Ollie:	OK, cool, what time do you want to meet up?
Keeley:	About eight. Are you coming then?
Ollie:	Yeah, I should be able to.
Keeley:	*(Light hearted tease.)* Sounds like the parents might be getting in the way there.
Ollie:	No, it'll be fine.
Keeley:	Well, I've got to go, but… it would be good to see you there.
Ollie:	Likewise.
Keeley:	Right. See you later.
Ollie:	Laters.

They both exit.

*This scene takes place at the Rec, the group's usual hangout. Mouse enters carrying a radio that he found in the class earlier. He should strut in comically to a dance/ hip hop track (perhaps **Sir Mix A lot's – Baby got back**) shortly followed by Steph.*

Steph:	Mouse, if you don't turn that crap off, I'm going to kill you!
Mouse:	You're just jealous coz I nicked it before you could!
Steph:	Mouse, why would I want to nick some dodgy old radio? That's kids stuff.
Mouse:	What?
Steph:	Well, who's going to buy that heap of crap?
Mouse:	*(Becomes very protective and defensive of his radio and begins speaking very quickly.)* No one! It's mine! I nicked it, I keep it. You're just saying it's crap so I think it's crap and then you'll wanna buy it off me for like a fiver or summin and I'll be thinking what an idiot for paying a fiver for that piece of crap and then you'll be laughing that you've actually got a pretty good radio for only a fiver and then you'll go an sell it on for like £50, and that wouldn't be a very nice thing to do!
Steph:	What?
Mouse:	What?
Steph:	Oh, shut up Mouse!
Mouse:	What?

Keeley enters.

Steph:	I'm gonna bang him out, I swear!
Keeley:	What's up with you?
Steph:	It's him! He never shuts up!
Mouse:	What?

Section 4

Steph:	Will you stop saying 'what'!
Mouse:	*(Confused)* Why?
Steph:	Because it's really ann… shut up! Look, just stop talking OK, Mouse?
Mouse:	*(In a slightly defensive tone.)* I don't see why you're getting so lairy…
Steph:	Mouse!
Mouse:	I'm only saying that you're over react…
Steph:	I'm warning you!
Mouse:	I think you just need to chill out a…
Steph:	For god's sake shut up!
Mouse:	What?

Steph loses her rag and lunges for Mouse's arm and twists it round behind his back, forcing Mouse to the ground.

Mouse:	Get off me you psycho!
Keeley:	*(Entering)* Steph, get off him! What's the matter with you?
Steph:	Nothing, as long as you keep that fruitcake out of my way!
Keeley:	Are you OK Mouse?
Mouse:	*(Lapping up the attention.)* I think so… *(Quietly, as if just about to cry)* She tried to pull my arm off!
Keeley:	*(Comforting)* Aww I'm sure she wouldn't have done. Look, why don't you go and listen to your radio eh, that'll cheer U up!
Mouse:	*(Still feeling sorry for himself)* Yeah, OK.

Mouse walks over to pick up his radio and, as he does so, he looks back at Steph and pokes his tongue out at her. They all sit silent for a moment as if thinking of things to do, clearly bored!

Section 4

Mouse:	Isn't Oxford boy supposed to be coming down tonight?
Steph:	*(Clearly not happy with the idea.)* What?
Keeley:	Yeah, dunno what time though.
Mouse:	I did wonder why you've got yourself all tarted up.
Keeley:	I have not!
Steph:	What the hell have you invited him down for?
Mouse:	He seems alright to me.
Steph:	*(Puts on a posh accent to mimic Ollie.)* Hi, I'm Ollie, Ollie Hammond and I've just moved down from Oxford don't you know… What a dickhead.
Keeley:	He doesn't talk anything like that!
Steph:	I bet he used to though, he is from Oxford!
Mouse:	I heard he got expelled from his old school.
Steph:	What for… Bending his ruler?
Mouse:	*(Mouse laughs along with Steph.)* Sounds like he was a right rebel.

At this point, Ollie appears and walks over to the group.

Keeley:	That's all right, I like a bit of rough.
Mouse:	Hiya Ollie! *(To Keeley)* You were saying?

Keeley turns round in horror to see Ollie standing right behind her. She quickly turns back round again.

Keeley:	*(Under her breath)* Shit!
Ollie:	Hiya guys. Sorry I'm late. *(They all greet him with the exception of Steph.)* So… what you up to?
Mouse:	Not a lot. Steph tried to pull my arm off!
Ollie:	What?

Keeley:	Don't worry. Did you have any trouble with your parents?
Ollie:	Nah, they were cool.
Steph:	*(Slightly confrontational)* Get a lot of grief from your parents, do ya?
Ollie:	*(Wary)* Not really!
Steph:	My dad wouldn't dare give me any grief, coz he knows what he'd get back. *(Slowly starts walking towards Ollie, trying to intimidate him.)* You've got to show 'em who's boss… isn't that right Ollie?

There is a pause and the atmosphere becomes tense. Mouse doesn't like what he sees and jumps in to break things up, using his radio as a distraction.

| Mouse: | Ollie, look what I nicked from school! Cool, eh! |
| Ollie: | *(Laughing at the idea of nicking something so stupid and Mouse's obvious excitement over it.)* Yeah, nice one Mouse. |

There is another moment of tension as the pair stand staring at each other, saying nothing.

Keeley:	*(To Ollie)* What's in the bag?
Ollie:	Eh?
Keeley:	The bag! What's in it?
Ollie:	Oh right, I brought a few beers along.
Mouse:	Nice one mate.
Keeley:	Aww! That's so sweet. Cheers Ollie.
Mouse:	*(To Steph)* See, I told you he was alright.

Ollie starts dishing out the cans as Steph turns and walks off to the other side of stage, clearly not happy. Ollie sees her and walks over to her with a can.

| Ollie: | Are you going to have one, or are you going to sit here sulking all night? |

Steph: Yeah, I'll have one… but can you keep up with me?

*There is another moment of tension between the two. Ollie walks off and Mouse finds a tune on his stereo. (A remix of **The Jam's - A Town called Malice** was used in the original production.) The choreographed sequence then begins and, during this, Ollie and Steph are involved in a drinking competition. The rest are equally wild and the whole scene should exude energy! The music suddenly changes to something more sinister, as does the whole mood of this section. One of the group has noticed Old man Harris staring at them out of his window. The group start to focus their attentions on him. Ollie looks a little concerned at first but slowly feels obliged to back up his new mates, for fear of rejection.*

Keeley: Hey guys, look who it is!

All: Old man Harris!

Keeley: Apparently we're being too rowdy!

Steph: Is that right Harris? Well, just turn your hearing aid down and you won't here us, will ya!

They all laugh.

Keeley: Yeah, go back to your pipe and slippers Grandad.

Mouse: I'm nowhere near your car.

Steph: Why should we move? It's a free country. You move!

Ollie: What's the problem? We're not hurting you!

Mouse: Scum? Who do you think you're calling scum?

The last line provokes the group and they begin getting very aggressive towards Old man Harris. The following lines can be spoken in turn but may be more effective if said over the top of one another.

Keeley: I'm a lil slapper, am I?

Ollie: You wanna watch your mouth mate.

Steph:	Who you calling a slapper? Come down here and say that, I'll bang you out!
Mouse:	You wanna get a life you sad old git!
Steph:	Well, why don't you come down here and shut me up then?
Keeley:	Gonna call the old bill are ya? I'm so scared.
Mouse:	Jog on Grandad!
Keeley:	Who cares if you know where I live?
Ollie:	Ain't you got anything better to do than give us grief?
Mouse:	I said I never touched your car, you deaf or summin?

Everyone apart from Steph becomes quiet.

Steph:	Go on then, phone the old bill, see if I care... tell you what, I'll give you something to moan about!

Steph moves across to the scaffolding and starts kicking it violently as if perhaps kicking Mr Harris' car. The rest of the group cheer her on. In the original production an actual car was set SL and it was this that was kicked. The lights fade to black as CCTV footage of a youth damaging property plays on the screen above. Mouse becomes Mr Harris and sits centre stage to deliver the following monologue to the audience. The group should be lit very slightly, with the main focus being placed on Mr Harris. The rest of the cast freeze in intimidating poses around the scaffolding, watching Mr Harris.

Mr Harris:	I only came out to see what the noise was about. When I saw one of them leaning on my car I asked them to get off. Then the trouble started. Suddenly they were shouting and swearing at me. There were four or five of them and they either had baseball caps or hoodies on, so I couldn't see their faces clearly. It was really intimidating. I didn't think I had said anything that bad. I had just asked them to get off my car. But this seemed to have been all the excuse that was needed.

(The cast take a couple of slow steps closer to Mr Harris.) They started to move closer to me getting more and more angry. By now I was really worried about what they might do, so I started to go back inside. I heard a thud and realised that one of them was kicking dents in the side of the car.

(The cast then hit the scaffolding.)

Why?... I had worked so hard to afford that car... it wasn't fair... it wasn't fair.

The actors then change position for the next scene.

Keeley and Steph enter SL into their house after a night at the Rec. Keeley is looking around for signs of anyone being home and is deflated but is not surprised when she notices they are not.

Keeley: I'm guessing Dad's still at the pub.

Steph: No surprises there then.

Keeley: What is it with everyone in this house?

Steph: What's that supposed to mean?

Keeley: You're both selfish, you and Dad. I mean what was all that crap with Ollie tonight? You know I like him but you're more concerned about giving it the big one in front of him.

Steph: Is that what you think?

Keeley: Yeah it is! And I tell you what; I know exactly what you're trying to do.

Steph: And what's that?

Keeley: Since Mum left, you've never let me have a life of my own. Any bloke that has ever come near me you've somehow managed to scare off. You can't keep doing this.

Steph: What are you talking about? It's got nothing to do with Mum leaving.

Keeley: Well what then… do you fancy him, is that it?

Steph: Look, believe it or not I've got better things to do than waste my time with goons like that!

Keeley: What, like making my life a misery.

Steph: Oh change the record!

Keeley: No! You can't control my life Steph… I know what's best for me, no one else. I actually want to make something of my life believe it or not and I'll do it my own way! …Oh what's the point, you never listen to me… I'm going to bed; I've got to be up early for the college open day.

| Steph: | What? You're not still on about going to college, are you? |

The lighting becomes suddenly very dark and tightly focused around the actors. A sound effect plays a sequence of something outside their house being broken, a key being fumbled in a door lock. The door then slams shut and we hear a few muffled footsteps before hearing an interior door squeak open. The following dialogue plays out over this sequence and should be timed so that Steph is alone in the room by the time we hear the interior door open.

| Keeley: | *(Looking around nervously.)* Shit, Dad's back. |

| Steph: | *(Becoming very anxious)* Great, he sounds pissed as usual. *(To Keeley)* Look, just go upstairs, I'll deal with it. |

| Keeley: | Please don't argue with him. |

| Steph: | Just go, will ya. *(Keeley quickly exits. Steph remains nervous until 'Dad' walks in. She then begins talking to this 'invisible' father figure.)* |
| | Hiya Dad… No, we've been back ages… I'm not lying… We were only a bit late… Let me make you a cup of coffee?… Sorry… Dad, don't be like this, it's not fair. *(Backing away.)* Look, I've said I'm sorry, I'm really sorry. |

Steph staggers back into the centre scaffolding as if she has been punched in the face. She then falls to her knees clutching her stomach as if it has just been kicked. The other cast members bash on the scaffolding, out of sight, as each blow is received. Once Steph collapses, the lights briefly fade to black.

Steph quickly exits and the lights change to represent Ollie's bedroom. Ollie enters. He turns on his computer console and mimes playing a game. Shortly after, Phillip and Sue enter and look at Ollie disapprovingly.

| Ollie: | What? |

| Sue: | *(Looking at Phillip.)* Your dad's had a call from Mr Bernard, your Head of Year. |

| Ollie: | *(Long sigh)* Ohhh. |

Sue:	Look Ollie, it's not on! He says that your school work is going downhill fast. That you started well but now you are late to lessons, not doing homework and being disruptive in class.
Ollie:	It's not that bad.
Phillip:	Isn't it? I thought we had gone through this before. This is your second chance… no, your last chance. What is the matter with you? Was being evicted from our home not a big enough warning for you?
Sue:	What is it going to take before you wake up and realise what you are doing to our family.
Ollie:	You're not family, Sue!
Phillip:	Now, that's enough! Sue's done a lot for you so have a bit of respect. You can't keep using your mother's death as an excuse Ollie. She's gone and you have to accept that and start taking some responsibility for your own life!
Ollie:	*(Going to leave)* I'm not standing here listening to this. *(Ollie exits.)*
Sue:	Yeah, that's it. Run away like you always do.
Phillip:	Sue! You'll only make things worse!
Sue:	Worse? How can things get any worse?
Phillip:	I know he's not easy to deal with…
Sue:	That's an understatement…
Phillip:	But he's still my son!
Sue:	I know, but we are running out of options… Maybe we should spend more time with him.
Phillip:	He doesn't want to be hanging around with us Sue.
Sue:	I think that's exactly what he needs!
Phillip:	I'm not sure…

Sue:	Is there any harm in trying? Why don't we all do something together… fishing or I don't know… camping one weekend?
Phillip:	Camping!?
Sue:	We've got nothing to lose!
Phillip:	Alright, fine. But I don't think its going to make any difference.
Sue:	Thanks… Why don't you give him a call on his mobile?
Phillip:	Alright. I'll phone him in a bit… give him time to cool off.

Sue throws her arms round Phillip and gives him a big hug. They exit the stage as Ollie enters to powerful dance music. Ollie is clearly angry and frustrated. This is displayed through a carefully choreographed sequence in which he throws himself around the stage, kicking, punching and shouting at anything that gets in his way.

This could be a nice opportunity to use the other members of the cast to bring on items or images relating to Ollie's past or his antisocial behaviour. Perhaps even bringing on signs or objects with words printed on them which Ollie can smash up in turn. Opportunities are also there for multimedia images to be used to help highlight his anger. This sequence should end up with Ollie dropping to the floor exhausted and very upset. At this point Keeley enters and finds him.

Keeley:	Ollie? *(She walks over to him.)* Wh… what's the matter?
Ollie:	*(Drying his eyes and putting on a brave face.)* I'm fine!
Keeley:	Yeah right, and I'm Britney Spears! Talk to me Ollie… is it your parents?
Ollie:	*(Uptight)* Parent! Sue's not my mum.
Keeley:	I guessed that she wasn't but I didn't want to ask. Where's your mum then?
Ollie:	She was killed in a car accident.

Keeley:	Oh my God, I'm sorry. How long ago?
Ollie:	Two years.
Keeley:	You must miss her.
Ollie:	More than anything.
Keeley:	I… I don't know what to say.
Ollie:	Don't worry, my dad and Sue had more than enough to say just now.
Keeley:	Do you get on with her?
Ollie:	Not a lot. I mean my mum's only been dead five minutes and he's already shacked up with someone else.
Keeley:	My mum left us when I was 12.
Ollie:	Really?
Keeley:	Yeah. It hit my dad pretty hard… that's when he started drinking.
Ollie:	Does he drink a lot?
Keeley:	Sometimes. I just try and stay out of his way. He picks on Steph mostly.
Ollie:	I'm sorry.
Keeley:	We're a right pair, aren't we?
Ollie:	Yeah.
Keeley:	So why are they so hard on you? Is it because you got expelled from your last school?
Ollie:	Well, it's not just that?
Keeley:	What do you mean?
Ollie:	There was some other stuff as well.
Keeley:	Like what?
Ollie:	Well, I kinda got into trouble once too many times.

Keeley:	I don't understand.

Ollie: Look, it doesn't matter.

Keeley: Come on Ollie, what is it?

Ollie: Well… because I kept getting into trouble… I was given…

Keeley: What?

Ollie: *(Hesitating about whether or not to tell Keeley about his ASBO)* I was given… a last chance?

Keeley: Your dad gave you that little 'last chance' speech, did he!

Ollie: Yeah… something like that.

Ollie's mobile phone starts ringing and he pulls it out of his pocket to see who it is. He doesn't want to answer it.

Keeley: Who is it?

Ollie: My dad.

Keeley: Answer it then.

Ollie: I've got nothing to say to him.

Keeley: Things won't get any better if you don't speak to him Ollie? *(Keeley stares at Ollie who still isn't answering the phone so she becomes impatient and snatches the phone off Ollie and answers it.)* Hi Mr Hammond, it's Keeley… yeah, I'm OK thanks… yep, he's right here next to me, I'll pass you over…

She holds the phone out for Ollie to take.

Ollie: What… yeah… I'm fine… *(Long pause)* OK… Has Sue put you up to this?… Camping?… Well, can I bring some of my mates?… *(Longer pause)*

Dad, are you there?… Ok… yeah, I'll see you at home a bit later. *(He hangs up).*

Keeley: What was that about?

Ollie:	Sue has obviously talked my dad into us all having some 'Bonding' time. He wants to know if we wanna go camping with them this weekend?
Keeley:	Yeh! That'll be a right crack.
Ollie:	Are you sure?
Keeley:	Yes. Why not?
Ollie:	I can just see them getting at me the whole time.
Keeley:	They won't if we are all there, surely. Oh come on.
Ollie:	I dunno?
Keeley:	We'll get to spend the whole weekend together!
Ollie:	*(Chuckling at Keeley's enthusiasm for the idea)* I'm not going to get out of this, am I?
Keeley:	Not if I can help it.
Ollie:	Alright.
Keeley:	This will be such a laugh.
Ollie:	It better be.
Keeley:	I can't wait to tell the others. *(Keeley runs off.)*
Ollie:	Oi, wait up! *(Ollie follows.)*

The lights fade to black.

Here is an opportunity to create some comical multimedia of the group in the forest. This could include attempting to put up tents, preparing a fire, playing pranks on each other in the dark and/or other camping related activities.

The lights then come up on the group who are now ready for bed in their tent on stage. This next part is accompanied by another video in the style of the 'Blair Witch Project', highlighting Keeley's fear and paranoia of camping.

Keeley:	What was that?
Mouse:	What?
Keeley:	That noise.
Mouse:	I didn't hear anything.
Keeley:	There it is again!
Mouse:	There's nothing there.
Keeley:	There bloody is.
Mouse:	Just relax a bit Keeley… it's probably only a mad axe man, or psychopathic killer. *(Mouse laughs)*
Keeley:	Ha bloody ha. I hate camping. Shit! *(She screams and sits up as if something is in her hair.)*
Ollie:	Keeley, will you shut up; you'll wake up the whole camp.
Keeley:	There's something in my hair! Get it out, get it out!
Mouse:	Keep still then… It's your hair clip, you dopey cow.
Keeley:	I hate camping!

Mouse begins fidgeting to make himself comfortable again.

Ollie:	Mouse, will you keep still.
Mouse:	It's this duvet and sleeping bag… it's not comfy.
Ollie:	How can it not be comfy? It must be like sleeping in a sauna.

Mouse:	*(Still fidgeting)* The floor is lumpy.
Keeley:	You've got a double airbed.
Mouse:	Right… nearly there…
Ollie:	*(Under his breath)* Finally.

The lights fade and the action pauses momentarily as Ollie falls back asleep. The lights then fade back up as we see Mouse trying to wake up Keeley.

Mouse:	Keeley… *(no reply)* Oi, Keeley.
Keeley:	*(Half-asleep)* What?
Mouse:	Look what I've brought. *(He gets out a bottle of vodka.)*
Keeley:	*(Whispering)* Ollie!
Ollie:	What?
Keeley:	Mouse has brought some vodka.

Mouse and Keeley start to leave the tent.

Ollie:	You're joking.
Keeley:	Oh come on, it'll be a laugh!
Ollie:	If my dad or Sue catches us I will be in deep shit.
Keeley:	What they don't know won't hurt them.

They all move downstage and begin drinking the vodka but Mouse has clearly already had a bit too much! They start to pass the bottle around, laughing. Ollie is starting to relax a bit. Meanwhile, Sue comes around to see what the noise is.

Sue:	What are you doing? *(Mouse and Keeley suppress a laugh.)* Ollie?
Ollie:	*(Looking around)* Nothing.
Sue:	Well, it is something. *(She sees the bottle.)* Who brought that? *(No one answers.)* I said who brought it? *(Silence.)*
Ollie:	*(Looking around.)* It was me.

Sue:	What?
Ollie:	It was me. I brought it.
Sue:	(Grabs bottle.) Get back to your tents.

(All of them start to head back to their tents but Sue stops Ollie in his tracks.) Not you! (Pause)

I trusted you… and this is how you repay me? Well what have you got to say? You've let me down Ollie, really let me down. (Sue walks back to her tent leaving Ollie looking guilty.)

We find the group (minus Steph) walking home after the day at school. Mouse and Ollie are kicking a can between them. All are laughing and joking around and discussing the camping trip.

Mouse: We should all go camping again. That was a right laugh.

Keeley: Well, you can count me out. I swear I've still got bugs crawling around in my hair. *(She starts scratching her head.)*

Mouse: You haven't!

Keeley: Shit, it's Steph, quick, change the subject.

Mouse: Right. So... um... Keeley, how was your date the other night?

Keeley: Yeah, it was good, apart from Ollie blubbing away like a baby through the whole film.

Ollie: I was not!

Keeley: You bloody were.

Ollie: For your information, I had a piece of popcorn in my eye!

Mouse and Keeley turn to look at each other.

Mouse & Keeley: *(Coughing and muttering under their breath.)* Bullshit!

Ollie: I did... alright... maybe I did have a tear in my eye at the end, but it was a sad film.

Mouse: What did you watch?

Keeley: Finding Nemo!

They all laugh out loud.

Ollie: *(Defensively)* He was lost!

Keeley: It's a fish!

Steph: Guess it just shows that you're not the big man you like to make out you are, doesn't it?

Keeley:	Steph!
Ollie:	What?
Steph:	It's pathetic.
Mouse:	You're the only one that's being pathetic Steph.
Steph:	Well well well, Little Mouse is getting a bit mouthy all of a sudden, isn't he.

She approaches Mouse menacingly.

Ollie:	Give it a rest Steph.
Keeley:	Yeah, pack it in will ya. Look, you lot coming in the shop?
Ollie:	You two go on, I'll be there in a minute.

Keeley realises that Ollie wants to have it out with Steph and tries to get him to leave it.

Keeley:	Please, come in with me.
Ollie:	I'll be in there in two minutes, don't worry.

Mouse and Keeley exit the stage.

Ollie:	So, what exactly is your problem?
Steph:	You are! I don't like you.
Ollie:	And why's that?
Steph:	You stroll in here like you own the place, trying to buy them all of with your free beers, not to mention my sister!
Ollie:	What about her?
Steph:	You know as well as I do that you're only using her till you find some other mug.
Ollie:	Is that right?
Steph:	You don't belong round here, this isn't Oxford now mate. If you carry on like you are, you gonna find yourself in trouble, and you don't want that.

Ollie:	I've had my fair share of troubles little girl, trust me! I can handle myself.
Steph:	Little girl? Come on then, what did ya do? Drop a tin of soup in Sainsbury's? Or were your library books late back?
Ollie:	Funny! But believe me; I'd make you look like an angel! Anyway, I don't have to explain myself to you! You're just jealous because Keeley's got a boyfriend and you don't. *(Mockingly.)* Aww what's up?... is little Steph getting lonely!
Steph:	Piss off goon. You don't know anything about me! But I'll tell you something… if you do want to stay with Keeley you better hope that someone doesn't make my dad think that you're leading his little girl astray.
Ollie:	Yeah, whatever.
Steph:	So, why did you come here?
Ollie:	I don't have to tell you anything.
Steph:	Oh come on goon. Do you really think I'd buy that crap story about your dad having a new job?
Ollie:	Well… it's the truth… he has got a new job.

Steph produces a page from a newspaper and begins reading out the article.

Steph:	"A council defended its decision today to evict a family from their privately rented home in Oxford. Phillip Hammond and Sue Warner were originally served with a warning following the antisocial conduct of Mr Hammond's 16 year old son, Oliver. Oliver Hammond was the subject of an Anti-Social Behaviour Order last December for spitting and swearing at neighbours, causing damage to property, theft and consistently causing alarm and distress to local residents".
Ollie:	And there was me thinking you couldn't read!

Steph:	Well, for a goon, you have been busy, haven't you? I just wonder how poor little Keeley will take it.
Ollie:	You bitch!
Steph:	Of course, she doesn't have to find out!
Ollie:	What's that supposed to mean?
Steph:	Just come down the Rec tonight.

Ollie exits, frustrated. Steph sits chuckling to herself for a while before exiting.

The rest of the cast surround Mrs Harris, edging closer in a menacing manner.

Mrs Harris:	It was the feeling of helplessness that was worst.
	A feeling that whatever we did, things wouldn't get any better; if we stood up to them, then we were just making ourselves targets. But if we ignored them, they would just keep on doing it anyway.
	The shouting, the laughing, being followed really close behind; they knew what scared people and they were bloody good at it. My husband was convinced we should say something to them, but what if it made it worse next time. A bottle through the window was one thing, but what if they decided to get really nasty. We tried calling the police…
All:	That was no good!
Mrs Harris:	Why can't they leave us alone? We just want to be left alone. *(Becoming more desperate looking at the people around her.)* Please go away. Just leave us alone!
All:	*(All, except Mrs. Harris, sarcastically mimicking last line). Just leave us alone! (They then all laugh before turning menacingly towards the audience.)*

We return to the Rec, where Keeley and Ollie are sitting alone. They are not speaking and Ollie seems quite agitated.

Keeley:	You would tell me if something was wrong, wouldn't you?
Ollie:	*(Abruptly)…* yes!
Keeley:	Well, something is obviously wrong?
Ollie:	Look, I said I'm fine, alright; now give it a rest, will ya!

Mouse, enters SR to hear Ollie losing his rag with Keeley.

| Keeley: | Fine! *(She storms off.)* |

Mouse walks over to find out what is wrong.

Mouse:	*(To Ollie)* What was all that about? You had a barney or something?
Ollie:	*(Annoyed.)* Don't you start as well.
Mouse:	Come on Ollie, you can speak to me.
Ollie:	Mouse, just leave it.
Mouse:	My mum always says that a problem shared is a problem solved… or is it halved? Oh, I dunno. But if you talk to me about it, then I can help.
Ollie:	No you can't!
Mouse:	Yeah I can. I know how you feel mate. Whenever I've got a problem I speak to my mum or dad about it and then things seem a bit…
Ollie:	*(Completely losing his rag.)* Just shut the fuck up, will you; You don't have a clue how I feel! You're a fucking loser Mouse; now get out of my face!

Mouse is completely taken aback by Ollie's onslaught and stands there speechless for a moment or two. Keeley stares over in disbelief. Steph enters looking pleased that Ollie's popularity within the group seems to have just taken a blow. Ollie exits.

| Steph: | Aww, you're not leaving already, are you Ol? |

Ollie stares back at her before he exits.

Mouse:	What's got into him?
Keeley:	*(Approaching Steph)* I dunno, but I'm pretty sure it got something to do with you!
Steph:	I dunno what you're talking about Kee.
Keeley:	Yeah right, you've never liked him!
Steph:	I swear I've not said anything to him. Look, if it makes you happy I'll go and have a word and get him to come back, alright?

Keeley:	Like he's going to listen to you!
Steph:	Oh he will, trust me!

Steph exits to go after Ollie.

| Mouse: | *(Trying to cheer her up.)* Come on Keeley, let's go up the chippy. *(There is not a lot of reaction from Keeley who looks really fed up.)* I'll treat ya to a pickled egg!? |
| Keeley: | *(Bringing a smile to her face.)* Thanks. |

They all exit the stage as the lighting changes to close in around Steph who re-enters and pulls a mobile phone out from her pocket. As she types a number into the phone, Mouse re-enters to pick up his mobile phone he has left behind, but Steph doesn't notice him. Mouse goes to leave once he collects his phone, but is stopped in his tracks by something Steph says on the phone.

| Steph: | *(Talking on the phone)* Hiya mate... it's Steph... yeah it's all sorted... he's coming down the Rec tonight... he's not going to know what hit him... yeah, or who... that's if he even has the bottle to turn up... can't wait to see that smug grin beaten off his face... anyway, thanks for this. I owe you one. See you. |

Steph hangs up the phone and exits. Mouse looks concerned and then pulls out his mobile phone, punches in a number and places the phone to his ear.

| Mouse: | Hi, is that Ollie's dad?... it's Mouse... Ollie's in trouble. |

The lights crossfade to the Rec again. It is later that night.

Steph:	Oh look it's Goons 'R Us!
Ollie:	What do you want?
Steph:	Well you see, I've got a bit of a problem. I need to get something but I can't do it on my own...
Ollie:	And what's that got to do with me?
Steph:	You're going to help me!

Ollie:	*(Laughing the idea off)* Dream on.
Steph:	As it stands, you don't seem to have a lot of choice. You're not exactly Mr Popular right now, are ya, and if you don't help me… well, then I guess I'll just have to tell Keeley about your ASBO and if she finds out you've been lying to her all this time, well…
Ollie:	You wouldn't dare.
Steph:	You know I would! So what's it gonna be?
Ollie:	Depends what it is?
Steph:	Old man Harris is having some work done on his house and the builders always leave their tools up there, and I want them!
Ollie:	Why do you want a load of tools?
Steph:	There's about a grand's worth of gear up there, it's easy money!
Ollie:	So what's in it for me?
Steph:	For you? Well, I'll keep my mouth shut about the ASBO for a start, Keeley won't find out you've been lying to her and I'll stay out of your way. You never know, it might even be a laugh.
Ollie:	I doubt that.
Steph:	So?
Ollie:	*(After a long pause.)* Alright… I'll help ya, but then I'm out, is that clear?
Steph:	Course.
Ollie:	Let's get it over with then.

*The pair walk over to the scaffold construction on the side of Old Man Harris' house as loud music plays. A mix of **T-Rex's – Children of the Revolution** was used in the original production.*

Ollie:	So where are they?

Steph:	Up on to top of that platform, now you're not afraid of heights, are you Ollie?
Ollie:	Just get up there and keep your voice down, eh.
Steph:	Ladies first!

They begin climbing the scaffolding, Ollie first, followed by Steph.

Ollie:	So where's the stuff?
Steph:	What would happen if you got caught now?
Ollie:	What?
Steph:	If anyone caught you now, what would happen?
Ollie:	Well... I'd... um... get arrested, look can we just get on with this. Now where are all the tools?

Steph begins chuckling to herself and becomes quite cocky.

Steph:	Ah that's right, there aren't any.
Ollie:	What?
Steph:	I was just curious to find out if you actually had the bottle to go through with it. I'm impressed.
Ollie:	Have you any idea how much trouble I could get into, just by being up here!
Steph:	*(Being smug)* Chill out, you're free to go.
Ollie:	Don't worry, I'm off...
Steph:	Although, I suppose I better introduce you to a mate of mine first.

The lights snap to the other side of stage where we see the actor playing Mouse appear as an unknown youth, dressed in a black hoody with his face covered up.

*Appropriate music begins to fade up over this next section. A mix of the **Prodigy's – Smack My Bitch Up** was used in the original production.*

| Ollie: | You've set me up! |

Steph:	Well you should have left my sister alone!
Ollie:	*(Grabbing Steph by the collar.)* What the fuck do you think you are doing?
Steph:	You've had it coming to ya, now get your hands off me. *(Pushing Ollie away from her)* I said get off me!

At this point, a stylised slow motion fight happens between Ollie and Steph on the scaffolding. This should be timed to the rhythm of any chosen music. After a few punches are thrown by Steph, Ollie finally snaps and pushes Steph with such force that she falls off the scaffolding. Staging this fall effectively will be a challenge but was successfully staged in the original production by using music, video, lighting and an additional scaffolding section connected to the side of the main scaffold construction. This was then lowered to the ground by the other members of the cast as Steph stands on it and flails her arms in slow motion. As Steph hits the ground, Ollie bolts down the scaffolding only to be stopped by Steph's hooded accomplice who tries to catch him trying to get away. As he catches him, Phillip enters and sees Ollie being beaten up.

Phillip:	Ollie! *(Running over to him and grabbing the attacker.)* Get off him!

Phillip is then set upon by the attacker. This attack needs to be staged as realistically as possible. It should result in Phillip, unknowingly to the audience, being stabbed. He falls to the floor and the attacker runs off.

Ollie pulls himself up and sees another body lying on the ground. It takes a moment for him to realise that it is his dad. He crawls over to him.

Ollie:	Dad… are you OK?… Dad!

He rolls him over onto his back and feels something wet on his hand, then lifts it up to reveal that it is covered in blood. His dad has been stabbed.

Oh my God… Dad… Dad… I'm sorry!

The lights briefly fade to black as Ollie and his dad exit.

The lights then come up on Keeley as she enters SL; she is slowly walking home on her own. Mouse enters chasing after her, he looks agitated.

Mouse:	Keeley, wait up.
Keeley:	Hiya.
Mouse:	I've just been to see Steph. Are you OK?
Keeley:	I guess, no one is telling me what happened. Did Steph say anything to you?
Mouse:	*(Unconvincingly)* Well... not really.
Keeley:	She has, hasn't she... What the hell happened?... Mouse!
Mouse:	Ollie's been lying to you Keeley.
Keeley:	What do you mean?
Mouse:	They didn't move down here because his dad got a new job, they were evicted.
Keeley:	Evicted? Why?
Mouse:	Ollie was given an ASBO for all the trouble he caused when he was living in Oxford. They had to move.
Keeley:	He's got an ASBO?
Mouse:	Yeah. That night outside the shop, Ollie let it slip to Steph.
Keeley:	How do you know all this?
Mouse:	Steph's told me everything.
Keeley:	I'm such an idiot.

Keeley starts to walk off.

Mouse:	Keeley... Keeley, where are you going? *(Pause)* Nice one Mouse!

Mouse exits. The lights fade across to centre stage. Ollie is sitting on his bed, clearly deep in thought.

Keeley:	*(Off stage)* Hi, is Ollie here?
Sue:	*(Off stage)* Yeah, he's upstairs? Ollie… Ollie!
Ollie:	*(Subdued)* Yeah?
Sue:	Keeley's here.
Ollie:	OK.
Steve:	Go on up.

Keeley enters frustrated and agitated. The atmosphere is awkward between the two of them.

Ollie:	Hiya.
Keeley:	I hear your dad's going to be OK.
Ollie:	Yeah, he was lucky.
Keeley:	Lucky? I hardly think he's lucky, do you?
Ollie:	Please, not you as well.
Keeley:	Oh, I haven't even started yet Ollie. Have you heard about Steph? She could be paralysed Ollie… I hope you're happy now.
Ollie:	What?
Keeley:	You never liked her.
Ollie:	It's was an accident Kee…
Keeley:	What, just like you accidentally forgot to mention that you've got an ASBO!

Silence.

Keeley:	Yeah, I know all about it… You lied to me Ollie.
Ollie:	Look, you don't understand…
Keeley:	No, I don't.
Ollie:	I wanted to tell you, but I was worried you wouldn't want to be with me.

Keeley:	Oh spare me the sob story, will ya. I've got no sympathy for you Ollie. Yeah. I'm sorry you lost your mum but that doesn't give you the right to treat everyone around you like dirt! My mum did a runner on us years ago remember, but you don't see me going around pushing people off buildings.
Ollie:	It was an accident.
Keeley:	And your poor dad… he's done nothing but look out for you all of your life and you've thrown it back in his face. If I was him, I'd wash my hands of you. In fact Ollie, that's exactly what I'm gonna do.
Ollie:	Keeley wait!

Keeley storms out of Ollie's bedroom. There is a brief moment where Ollie sits with his head in his hands just before Sue shouts up to him again.

Sue:	Ollie, come down here.
Ollie:	Not now, Sue.
Sue:	Ollie, you need to come down.
Ollie:	*(Getting more desperate.)* Look, I said later!
Sue:	Ollie… the police are here.

Ollie stands up as if to leave his room but as he stands up on the top of the scaffolding he is lit only by a single white spotlight from above. He stands still facing the audience, with his hands behind his back as if handcuffed.

Judge:	*(Voice over)* Oliver Hammond, you have deliberately and consistently broken the conditions of the Anti-Social Behavioural Order issued to you. Despite the obvious remorse you have shown, following the tragic events on the night of the 27th, I have no alternative but to sentence you to an eighteen month detention and training order. Of this, you will spend the first nine months in custody.

Section 9

Ollie is sitting on one side of the stage in a Young Offenders Institution. Mouse enters and sits a little way from him. Ollie doesn't look up. There is an uncomfortable silence.

Mouse:	How are you Ollie?... I brought some stuff for you. *(He starts to rummage through a bag.)* They said I could bring it in, but it had to be checked first. It's not much, just some magazines and chocolate and stuff. My mum made a cake… *(Ollie looks up, holds eye contact, and then looks back down. Again there is an uncomfortable silence. Trying to be brighter).* School has finished now. I got four GCSEs… *(More silence.)*
Ollie:	How's Steph?
Mouse:	Well… not great. She is out of intensive care, but they still don't think she will walk… They're still doing lots of tests and stuff… It wasn't your fault mate.
Ollie:	*(Quite loudly.)* Do you think it bothers me that it wasn't added to my list of offences Mouse? *(Mouse goes to leave.)* No don't go. I'm sorry Mouse. It's just this place. I'm in here for another six months and it's doing my head in. Hardly anyone comes to see me. My dad hasn't spoken to me for ages, it's a bloody nightmare.
Mouse:	Your dad will come around mate. It'll just take time, that's all.
Ollie:	I doubt it. He is really hurt still.
Mouse:	I know, but he will.
Ollie:	Maybe… What are you doing now? You at college?
Mouse:	Nah, I'm not doing much. I help my dad sometimes.

Ollie:	…What about Keeley? Is she alright? I keep writing to her, but she hasn't answered. *(An awkward silence becomes apparent.)* Mouse, what is it? *(Still Mouse is silent.)* Mouse?
Mouse:	Sorry mate. *(Mouse hands Ollie a bunch of letters.)* She wants you to stop.

Ollie takes the letters and is obviously distraught.

Ollie:	I miss her Mouse.
Mouse:	I know mate… I know.

The lights fade to black.

THE END

School Nightmare (Deleted scene)

This scene has been deleted as it was superfluous to the piece, but it always went down a storm when performed by our group. Therefore we decided to include it in the book and leave it up to your judgement whether you want to use it or not. The scene can be inserted between sections 6 and 7.

The scene begins with Ollie's mum and dad talking about the trouble that Ollie has got into.

Sue:	I can't believe Ollie has got himself into trouble again. I really thought he was going to make a fresh start.
Phillip:	I know. He promised me it would be different this time. I just don't understand it?
Sue:	Well I blame the teachers…
Phillip:	What?
Sue:	… and that school he goes to.
Phillip:	I'm not sure we can blame the teachers?
Sue:	If we had paid for him to go to a private school, none of this would have happened.
Phillip:	But he was just the same at his old school. Perhaps it's us, maybe we haven't been giving him enough attention.
Sue:	Oh come on Phillip. He has got everything he needs. New clothes, latest trainers and that MP player thing. No, I blame the teachers. I'd love to know what they are teaching them.
Phillip:	Look, we'll talk again in the morning. I'll try and reason with him… goodnight love.
Sue:	*(Spoken as if dropping off to sleep.)* What do they teach them? What do they teach them? What do they te…

A dream sequence now starts as if they are in a classroom. The actor playing Ollie now enters as a teacher speaking in a very 'public school' manner. The actor playing Phillip becomes an additional pupil. Keeley becomes Pupil with lines.

Teacher:

Now then class, your English papers were, I fear, well below the standard I was expecting. Jenkins in particular, your summing up of the themes from the Wordsworth collection of poems was, quite frankly, disturbing. As for the rest of you, algebra was, again, quite unsatisfactory. And I think it only fair to warn you that the test I had scheduled for next Wednesday will, in fact, be moved forward to this Friday. *(Groans from Class)*. Now, I can only hope that you are going to show a far more positive attitude towards today's lesson, and will start to make up for the appalling inadequacies of your recent efforts. Today we are going to be examining the finer points of… gang warfare. And in particular this week we will be concentrating on acquisition of an appropriate firearm. As usual, to help us adopt a more convincing learning environment we will of course be speaking in the dialect of Hip Hop slang. *(More groans)*. So, to begin. White, *(Addressing a pupil)* from last week, what can you tell us about why you might need to obtain the said standard firearm? Or should I say, "So homie, what beef be kickin' off dat you gonna need to pop a cap in someone's ass?"

Pupil

Sir, do we have to do this?

Teacher:

White, I am not doing this for my benefit! Don't come crawling back to me when you leave this school and don't have a hope of getting a well paid pimping job. Now if you want to be a proper functioning member of society, you must pay attention.

Pupil:

Sorry sir.

Teacher:

So in answer to my question?

Pupil:

(Without any energy or enthusiasm.) If you dis me or ma bitch, I is gonna pay you back big time innit.

Teacher:	Respec Whitey. *(Also makes hand gesture of slapping his fingers together)*. Now, me is gonna show you how you's gets a piece, and the how to aks the right questions, aiight. So we needs a piece of hardware for specifick jobs. Now, me reckons that a good Magnum 45 is all you gonna need for a nice corner shop. But what is best for a bank job? Umm Whitey what does you fink?
Pupil:	Well, would it be most convenient… *(interrupted by teacher)*
Teacher:	Urrrmmm. *(Looking disapprovingly at her.)*
Pupil:	Well, me is gonna use a piece that gives me instant respect, an no pigs is gonna argue with me if I gots an Ouzi.
Teacher:	Big it up for Whitey class. *(Class reluctantly cheer and someone does a feeble whoop.)* Now, if yous really wants to make an impact how about a couple of hand grenades. *(He makes as if to pull the pins out and the class shriek.)*

The class then shriek and run out, chased by the teacher. Sue wakes up screaming. Phillip comes rushing in.

Philip:	Are you alright love?
Sue:	What are we going to do with him?

Bang Out of Order – GCSE cuts

Cut from (and including):	Cut to (and including):
p11 Mrs Harris: Will you come away from that window!	p12 Mr Harris: That's exactly why they think they can run riot 24 hours a day, because no one says anything.
p13 The top of the page.	p13 Sue: *(shouting after him)* Ollie… Ollie!
p13 The bottom of the second paragraph of stage directions where it says: *Once they are all ready, they begin to make their way round… etc*	p14 Mouse: *(Calling off stage.)* Mum, have you made my sandwiches?... etc
p14 Keeley: Great, another shitty day at school.	p15 *The bell goes and they start to make their way to lessons.*
p21 Steph: What the hell have you invited him down for?	p21 Keeley: *(under her breath)* Shit!
p23 Keeley: Apparently we're being too rowdy!	p24 Stage directions up to and including: *Steph moves across to the scaffolding and starts kicking it violently as if perhaps kicking Mr Harris' car. The rest of the group cheer her on. In the original production an actual car was set SL and it was this that was kicked.*
p26 Cut from the top of the page.	p27 Stage directions, up to and including: *Steph quickly exits and*

Bang Out of Order – GCSE cuts

p28 Phillip: Sue! You'll only make things worse!	p29 Stage directions only up to and including: *Sue throws her arms around Phillip and gives him a big hug.*
p31 Keeley: Your dad gave you that little 'last chance' speech did he!	p36 Keeley: Shit, it's Steph, quick, change the subject. *You will also need to amend Mouse's next line to:* Mouse: Keeley, how was your date the other night?

p37 Amendment to Keeley's line at the top of the page should be made to: Keeley: Steph! Look I'm going to the shop. I don't need this. *(Keeley and Mouse exit)*

p37 Ollie: What?	p37 Ollie: And why's that?
p39 Steph: Just come down the Rec tonight.	p39 To the bottom of the page.
p40 *We return to the Rec, where Keeley and Ollie are sitting alone. They are not speaking and Ollie seems quite agitated.*	p42 Keeley: *(Bringing a smile to her face)* Thanks.
p43 Ollie: Let's get it over with then.	p44 Steph: I was just curious to find out if you actually had the bottle to go through with it. I'm impressed.

p44 Ollie: Don't worry I'm off. - **Note: This is a single line cut.**

p46 From top of the page.	p48 Sue: Ollie… the police are here.

For more pictures of the original
productions, examples of multi-media
and clips of the movement sequences,
log on to:

www.bangoutonline.co.uk

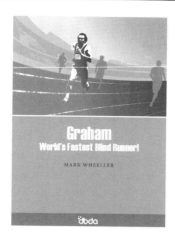

ISBN 978 1 902843 26 1

Cast: 6 (3m, 3f with doubling). Can be performed with a cast of up to around 30. (10m, 8f & 12 m or f)
Duration: 55 minutes
Suitable for: ages 13+ or adults!

Developed from Mark Wheeller's stage play Race To Be Seen, written with the Epping Youth Theatre.

Graham - World's Fastest Blind Runner!

Written in the same documentary style as Too Much Punch For Judy, Mark's first version of this play about Graham Salmon MBE, was awarded Critics Choice at the Edinburgh Festival Fringe (1984). It has recently been re-written, and on it's first two outings won through to the Final of both the National Drama Festivals Association in 2007 and the All England Theatre Festival in 2008, winning different awards at each Festival.

Listed in the Guiness Book of Records as The Worlds Fastest Blind Runner in 1976 (100m in 11.4 secs) Graham went on to play Golf for the international visually impaired team for whom he hit a famous "hole in one" in The British Open!

"I didn't ever need convincing that 'Graham' was an ideal piece to challenge my group and that it ticked all the boxes for A-level work, but if I ever needed justification, then the results have certainly given it. In the breakdown of the Unit 2 marks i.e. the performance of 'Graham', all seven candidates were awarded 100%. It's worth noting that the external moderator was accompanied that evening by her senior examiner! Thanks again for the material and thanks to Graham, such an inspirational person!"

Mike Fleetwood, Parkside Arts College.

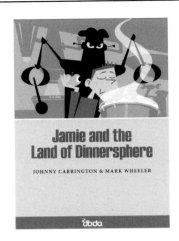

Jamie and the Land of Dinnersphere

JOHNNY CARRINGTON & MARK WHEELER

dbda

ISBN 978 1 902843 25 4

Cast: *2m and 2f with doubling or 3m, 1f and 5 or 6m/f. Suitable for use as a TIE production in the new vocational courses for ages 13+ (or as a performance piece in Primary schools)*
Duration: *35 minutes (55 minutes with the workshop)*

NEW! – JAMIE AND THE LAND OF DINNERSPHERE
(a Healthy school dinners play) by Johnny Carrington & Mark Wheeller

Jamie Jamjar loves healthy food. He has seen how a poor diet can mess you up… just by looking at his sister… Lazy Lillian! Jamie is shocked when his school tries out the new Robot Dudes (fast food servants) who replace the friendly dinner ladies. Jamie then discovers his own father invented them!

Can it get any worse? Yes it can!

Jamie is transported to Dinnersphere (in another of his father's inventions, a Story Rocket) where Jamie discovers the nefarious Dinnerwitch, busy planning world domination through putrid school dinners! Together with three friends, Bo, Agor and another - a member of the Primary School audience - they confront and defeat the Dinnerwitch!

Jamie provides an opportunity for secondary school students to present an interactive Theatre In Education play with all the joys of the audience being a key part of the final performance. It is expected to become a staple part of the new vocational courses where there are, at the moment, few plays which will fit the specification so well!

The text includes an innovative interactive workshop written by Adrian New (Stopwatch Theatre) which can be led by the secondary students.

Mark Wheeller

KILL JILL!

ISBN 978 1 902843 20 9

Cast: *11+ (3m, 3f & 5 m or f)*
Suitable for GCSE with doubling
(2m, 2f & 1 m or f)
Duration: *50 minutes approx.*
Suitable for: *ages 13+*
or adults!

Commissioned and
premiered by The
Birmingham Rep Theatre

NEW! – KILL JILL
by Mark Wheeller

Big Brother meets Kill Bill meets Jack (of Beanstalk fame) meets Tony Martin… Mix these together to create *Kill Jill!* This brand new play by Mark Wheeller explores the topical issues of homeowners defending themselves, and asks "How far can Reality TV be allowed to go?"

Jill is the latest victim of Reality Lottery, a futuristic form of National Service to entertainment. She accompanies Jack as he (again) robs George, who lies in wait armed with a shotgun. The Reality Lottery camera operators are filming everything… but should they intervene? The ending is suitably Tarantinoesque!

Kill Jill! raises issues of rights and responsibilities. It is a play full of interesting techniques that will delight Drama teachers and students, and will thrill those exploring Citizenship issues through imaginative and entertaining Theatre productions.

'Kill Jill is a very fizzy ride! What a great script! The playfulness with style and wide range of reference points with an 'anytime, anyplace, anywhere' theatrical freedom… the banter goes to some strange places too - perhaps a Python influence? The build up of tension in the visit to George's castle puts the end of the play in firm thriller territory! Wonderful stuff!!!!!'

Paul Mills, Head of Drama,
Westgate School, Winchester

Other plays published by **dbda**

ISBN 1 902843 17 1

Cast: *33f, 3m &3m/f or 3m & 3f for GCSE using suggested cuts*
Duration: *55 minutes approx.*
KS 3 & 4.

Gagging for it by Danny Sturrock

Summer is here, A-levels are over and a group of 6 friends embark on a holiday to Ibiza! What would their holiday bring? Would Chris finally pluck up the courage to ask out Teresa? Would Jay drink himself into oblivion? Would Bianca spend the entire holiday flirting with the Spanish barmen – more than likely! ...or would their experiments with drugs bring their hedonistic worlds crashing down around them!?

Comedy, dance music and choreography are the keys to this production. The pace is breakneck and hilarious, but once the party's over, it hits you!

'Really funny... laugh out loud funny. Inspired outstanding performances from the six Year 11s who went on to exceed our expectations by a long way in their GCSEs achieving A or A*. It proved to be a firm favourite with our KS3/4 audience.'

Mark Wheeller

ISBN 1 902843 18 5

Cast: *32f & 2m with doubling*
Duration: *60 minutes approx.*
KS 3 & 4 and A Level

Legal Weapon II by Mark Wheeller

This is a new "improved" version of the popular Legal Weapon play which is touring schools across the UK.

It is the story of a young man, Andy. His relationship with his girlfriend – and his car – are both flawed, but his speeding causes the loss of a life and the loss of his freedom.

In Legal Weapon II, the story takes an additional twist when Andy realises that the person he's killed is somebody very dear to Jazz, his girlfriend.

Legal Weapon II promises to be faster, funnier and far more powerful!

'A gripping storyline. Even the most challenging of our students were held by the drama. This learning experience should be given to each Year 11 as they come through the school.'

Myrtle Springs Secondary School

The Gate Escape by Mark Wheeller

The story of two truants. Corey is 'addicted' to bunking school. Chalkie views himself as a casual truant "no problem!" While truanting with some friends, the pair are greeted by a surreal 'Big Brother' figure who sets them a task. The loser will be in for some dramatic 'Big Bother'... Who will lose?... What will this 'bother' be?

The play has toured professionally throughout the south of England to great acclaim.

'A lively dramatic style and innovative structure with dynamic and contemporary dialogue. It is written in a way to guarantee that the audience will feel fully involved and enthralled by the main characters.'

ISBN 978 1 902843 22 3

Professor Ken Reid, Author of Tackling Truancy in Schools

Cast: *2f & 2m with doubling, or up to 30*
Duration: *70 minutes*
KS 3 & 4.

'Theatrically interesting... excellent basis for active discussion of issues and dramatic style with reluctant GCSE students'

Ali Warren (National Drama)

Heroin Lies by Wayne Denfhy

A sensitive, yet disturbing look at drugs and drug dependency, in particular the pressures and influences at play on an ordinary teenage girl. We observe Vicki's gradual and tragic slide towards addiction and also the various degrees of help and hindrance she receives from family and friends.

This is a new, updated edition of Wayne Denfhy's popular play. It is suitable for performance as well as for reading in the class. Included with the playscript is an excellent scheme for follow-up work by Peter Rowlands.

ISBN 1 902843 15 0

Cast: *8f, 7m and 2m/f*
Duration: *70 minutes approx.*
KS 3 & 4

'...a piece of drama that will stimulate and challenge a young cast... Heroin Lies deals with vital issues that affect today's youngsters in a gentle and humane way and, in so doing, gets its message across without the instant rejection that can meet other approaches.'

Pete Sanpher, Head of Drama, Norfolk

Other plays published by **dbda**

CHICKEN! by Mark Wheeller
New Updated Edition

A 'new and improved' version of WHY DID THE CHICKEN CROSS THE ROAD? The play tells the story of two cousins, Tammy and Chris. We are led to believe that something bad will happen to Chris who refuses to wear his cycle helmet. It is, however, Tammy who gets killed on the one morning that the cousins walk to school. Chris remains unwilling to tell anyone of his part in the accident and he has to live with this dreadful secret. One of the main changes is the introduction of Chris filming Tammy's fatal dare on his mobile phone camera.

'We have just been fortunate enough to witness the most superb exhibition of interactive safety education. The performance was quite stunning!'

Jim Lambert, Head Teacher Sinclair Middle School, Southampton

ISBN 1 902843 19 3

Cast: *34m, 3f & 2m/f or 2m & 2f for GCSE*
Duration: *35 minutes approx.*
KS 3 & 4.

Hard to Swallow by Mark Wheeller

This play is an adaptation of Maureen Dunbar's award winning book (and film) **Catherine** which charts her daughter's uneven battle with anorexia and the family's difficulties in coping with the illness.

The play has gone on to be performed all over the world to much acclaim, achieving considerable success in One Act Play Festivals. Its simple narrative style means that it is equally suitable for adult and older youth groups to perform.

'This play reaches moments of almost unbearable intensity... naturalistic scenes flow seamlessly into sequences of highly stylised theatre... such potent theatre!'

Vera Lustiq, The Independen

ISBN 978 1 902843 08 7

Cast: *3f & 2m with doubling, or 6f, 3m & 16*
Duration: *70 minutes approx.*
KS 3 to adult

'Uncompromising and sensitive... should be compulsory viewing to anyone connected with the education of teenagers.'

Mick Martin, Times Educational Supplemen

WACKY SOAP by Mark Wheeller

Script & Lyrics by Mark Wheeller
Music by James Holmes

Wacky Soap

The Music Score

Includes a Mini-Musical for Junior Schools

Wacky Soap is a Pythonesque allegorical tale about 'substance' abuse (drugs, alcohol, glue, tobacco, etc). While washing with Wacky Soap leads to instant happiness and an inclination towards outrageous behaviour, prolonged use washes away limbs and ultimately leads to dematerialisation. This has become a tried and tested (and increasingly popular) School/ Drama Club/ Youth Theatre production and is an ideal vehicle for a cast of any age.

'Wacky Soap is a brilliant show for any age group. It has the "Wow factor" not the "Yawn factor" so often associated with educational material. The script is fast and comical. The songs are wonderfully catchy. The Audience at the end were calling for more'.

Sally Dwyer, Hants Drama Teacher/ Eastleigh Borough Youth Theatre Director

ISBN 1 902843 06 1

The full version of the Musical play which includes scheme of work for KS3/4.

The story of Wacky Soap first appeared as a full **Musical play.** A mini version of the play is included with the **Music Score.** The **Storybook,** as well as being a wonderful book to read on its own, is often used for inspiration with props and costumes for the play. **A Past-performance CD** gives you the opportunity to hear the songs of the play, while a fully orchestrated **Backing track CD** is invaluable for those who want to produce the play but do not have music facilities.

The Story of
WACKY SOAP
A Cautionary Tale

Mark & Rachael Wheeller
Illustrations by Geoffrey Griggs

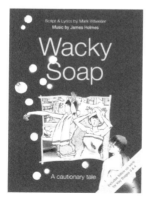

Script & Lyrics by Mark Wheeller
Music by James Holmes

Wacky Soap

A cautionary tale

ISBN 1 902843 07 X

A fully illustrated book with the story of Wacky Soap in narrative form.

ISBN 1 902843 02 9

*A companion book with the Music Score and a **Mini-Musical** version of the play.*

Past Performance and Backing track CDs

Other Plays by Mark Wheeller (not published by **dbda**)

Sequinned Suits And Platform Boots
Duration: 55 mins   Cast: 6f, 7m & 1m or f
Published by: Maverick Musicals: http://www.mavmuse.com/default.asp

A play that seems more like a Musical! Sequinned Suits and Platform Boots is Mark Wheeller's new One Act comedy tribute to the colourful Glam Rock years. It charts (semi-autobiographically) the teenage years of Shakey Threwer and his desperate attempt to be noticed by the Music industry. "Funky & funny… but be warned, it will have you coming away cringing at your own memories of singing into a hairbrush whilst staring at your reflection in the mirror." Craig Morrison Southampton Institute Newspaper 2005

Arson About   Script: Mark Wheeller (Ed. Andy Kempe)
Duration: 75 mins   Cast: 4 (2f & 2m with doubling)
Published by: Nelson Thornes Ltd. Tel: 01242 267100

Mollie and Ian are hot for each other. Stueey can be a real bright spark. Mr Butcher's comments have inflamed Shuttle. All in all it's combustible material but when you play with fire it can be more than your fingers that get burnt. Arson About is a theatrical power keg which crackles with wit and moves along with a scorching pace. But in this play by Mark Wheeller the cost of 'Arson About' becomes all too clear.

Chunnel of Love   Script: Graham Cole & Mark Wheeller
Duration: 100 mins Cast: 25 (11f, 8m & 6m/f)
Published by: Zig Zag Education. Tel: 0117 950 3199

A bi-lingual play (80% English & 20% French) about teenage pregnancy. Lucy is fourteen - she hopes to become a vet and is working hard to gain good grades in her GCSE exams, when she discovers she is pregnant. She faces a series of major decisions, not least of which is what to tell the father... Ideal as a school production and Key Stage 4 Drama course book.

Sweet FA!   Script: Mark Wheeller   Duration: 45 mins plus interval
Cast: 3f / 2m (or more)
Published by: *SchoolPlay Productions Ltd. Tel: 01206 540111*

A Zigger Zagger for girls (and boys)! A new play (also available as a full length Musical) telling the true life story of Southampton girl footballer Sarah Stanbury (Sedge) whose ambition is to play Football (Soccer) for England. Her dad is delighted ... her mum disapproves strongly! An ideal GCSE production and Key Stage 4 Drama course book. Drama GCSE scheme of work also available.

Blackout – One Evacuee in Thousands (MUSICAL)
Script: Mark Wheeller with the Stantonbury Youth Theatre Music: Mark Wheeller
Duration: 90 mins plus interval   Published by: SchoolPlay Productions Ltd.

A Musical about the plight of Rachel Eagle, a fictional evacuee in World War II. Rachel's parents are determined that the war will not split the family up. After refusing to have her evacuated in 1939 they decide to do so midway though 1940. At first Rachel does not settle but, after the death of her mother, she becomes increasingly at home with her billets in Northamptonshire. When her father requests that she return she wants to stay where she feels at home. An ideal large scale school production with good parts for girls (and boys).

For more details and an up-to-date list of plays, please visit Mark's website:
www.amdram.co.uk/wheellerplays